# Tinseltoon

## or

# One Night in Newcastle

Christopher Goulding

illustrated by

Chris Mabbott

Tyne Bridge Publishing

Christopher Goulding first told this story to Becky, Sarah, Michael and Paul on New Year's Eve, 1994. He then read it on BBC Radio Newcastle in December 1995, and again on Christmas Day in 1996 and 1997. Since then the story of Tinseltoon has delighted thousands of children from Newcastle, and beyond.

Newcastle Libraries thank Fenwick Ltd for their support in the production of this new edition of Tinseltoon.

Tinseltoon was first published by Newcastle Libraries in 1998. This is a revised edition.

ISBN 978-185795-212-4

Published by City of Newcastle upon Tyne
Newcastle Libraries
Tyne Bridge Publishing
2012

Printed by Elanders UK, North Tyneside.

Late one Christmas Eve, maybe a minute before midnight, I was prowling around the rooftops of Newcastle city centre.

The streets were deserted, all the shops were shut, the pubs had closed, and the cinemas and theatres had all emptied. Everyone had gone home. There wasn't a soul about … except for me, Grainger the cat.

I was just walking past the Northern Goldsmiths shop on Pilgrim Street when I heard the bells of Saint Nick's Cathedral chiming midnight. I hadn't realised how late it was, so I looked up at the Goldsmiths clock to check the time and you'll never guess what I saw!

You know the golden fairy who stands up there all the year round …?

Well, just as the clock was striking midnight, the golden fairy came to life, bent her legs and did a great ballet dancer's leap from the top of the clock. She flew into the air and started flying round and round. I couldn't believe my eyes!

She darted and spun in the starry night sky above me. She was whooping and shouting and laughing with joy just to be free again after spending a whole year on top of that clock.

After she'd flown around for a few moments, she hovered in mid-air, and looked, with a great big smile on her face, at the Christmas lights twinkling away on Northumberland Street below.

She drew her right hand up above her head. Suddenly it was full of a bright sparkling tinsel dust that glittered and shone in the night.

Then I heard her speak: 'Now to wake up all the other statues!'

Off she flew up Northumberland Street, scattering her magic dust. The four statues that stand above one of the shops began to move, and leaped from their niches.

Then she flew high up into the sky and sped around the rest of the city sprinkling her dust on all the other statues, bringing them to life.

Then hovering above the city, she said this little rhyme:

'Once more the Eve of Christmas Day
Shall see Newcastle's statues play.
For minutes five before the morn
This city's streets I shall transform,
And by the light of the silver Moon
Newcastle shall be Tinseltoon!'

After that, as I strolled up Northumberland Street, I saw something incredible!

The four statues had jumped down from their places in the wall and were having a whale of a time. John Marley, the Cavalier Mayor of Newcastle from olden times, and Harry Hotspur, a knight in shining armour, were playing at sword fights …

Thomas Bewick was ambling down the street admiring the display in Fenwick's window.

Roger Thornton – another Mayor of Newcastle from days gone by – had noticed the little fun fair on Northumberland Street. He climbed up to the top of the helter-skelter and slid down it, screeching at the top of his voice!

And that was just in Northumberland Street!

I thought I'd take a quick walk around the town to see what else was going on … and there was plenty. You wouldn't believe the things I saw.

Earl Grey, on top of his monument, woke up, and then came sliding down the column, just like a fireman sliding down a pole. When he got to the bottom he danced and capered off down Grey Street towards the river, singing 'The Blaydon Races' at the top of his voice.

Up by the Hancock Museum, Lord Armstrong jumped down from his plinth, dusted the pigeon droppings from his shoulder and said, in a very posh voice, 'Hmm … think I'll saunter down to the Quayside and have a look at my Swing Bridge.' And off he went with a spring in his step, considering just how old he is.

Up at St James' Park, Jackie Milburn had started moving! He stretched himself and jumped down from his pedestal. His bronze football strip had changed to black and white.

Off he ran down the road, kicking his ball in front of him, bouncing it off the walls, heading it over the top of the lamp posts, doing keepy-ups using his knees, and shouting for joy like a little lad just let out of school.

Over at Saint Nick's Cathedral, the golden statues of Adam and Eve had flown down from the tower, and were capering around with no clothes on right in front of Queen Victoria. She was sitting on her throne in the Cathedral courtyard looking down on them with a sniffy expression on her face and saying 'Ooooh! We ARE NOT amused!'

And around the back of the Cathedral, the rabbit, with the great big teeth, from above the office doorway had hopped down and was nibbling at some grass in the churchyard.

On Neville Street, by the Central Station, George Stephenson and his four mates, who sit at his feet all day, had leaped down to the pavement and were dancing in a ring around their pedestal wearing orange traffic cones on their heads like party hats.

Within a few minutes, the city had become a playground full of strange, weird and wonderful characters cavorting around like there was no tomorrow.

The miner, from the top of Burt Hall, was dancing a Highland Fling with his pick on the ground instead of a claymore sword.

Saint George, from Old Eldon Square, was on his horse chasing the dragon up Blackett Street. The dragon was huffing and puffing fire and smoke all over the place!

Once all the city's statues had been woken up the golden fairy flew off to have her annual chat with her friend, the other golden fairy above the clock on Westgate Road.

But while she was away, things began to get out of hand — especially on the Quayside.

King Neptune, from the top of the old Fish Market building, climbed up onto the top of the Tyne Bridge, and was jumping off, doing dive-bombers into the river!

And there in the middle of the Swing Bridge was Lord Armstrong, spinning and whizzing in circles, using it like a merry-go-round …

And George Stephenson and his pals were riding George's old steam engine back and forth over the High Level Bridge, just like a giant train set!

And then they all leaped across the river to Gateshead to clamber over the Baltic, the Sage, and the Millennium Bridge!

Back on Northumberland Street, things had become quite rowdy. Jackie Milburn had arrived and organised a footy match with some of the other statues, and the game was getting fast and furious.

All of a sudden Jackie booted the ball towards the goal. Harry Hotspur didn't have a chance of getting his hands to it – to be fair, it's not easy being a goalkeeper when you're wearing a suit of armour. The ball flashed past him and banged straight into Fenwick's window.

Luckily the window didn't break, but the burglar alarm went off!

That was enough to bring the golden fairy whizzing back to find out what was happening.

'I don't know!' she said, 'I can't leave you alone for a minute'.

'Sorry! I didn't mean it,' said Jackie Milburn. 'It was an accident.'

The fairy looked stern.

'You know better than to play football in the street with all these windows around.

'That's enough for now anyway. You've had your Christmas five minutes. Come on, it's time to get back up on your pedestals for another year.'

At this, some of the statues began to moan a bit. 'Aah, please – just one more minute!' said Thomas Bewick, who had been enjoying the game enormously.

'Not one minute more!' said the golden fairy. 'Just five minutes each Christmas. That's all you get. Now come along.'

And so all of the statues wearily dragged themselves up onto their pedestals. Just before the fairy put them all back to sleep for another year, she wished them all a Merry Christmas.

'Aye…' said Harry Hotspur in his broad Northumbrian twang, '…and a Merry Chrrrristmas to ye too, and thanks for waking wuz aal up forrr a bit o' fun once again. See ye next yeorrr, pet!'

'Good night Harry!' smiled the fairy, and with a wave of her hand the statues turned to stone once more.

Then she floated to the top of the Goldsmiths clock.

With one last look at the pretty lights twinkling in Northumberland Street, she stretched her arms above her head, turned her face to the stars, and froze once more into that beautiful pose we know so well.

As for me? Well, I'd had enough excitement for one night and I scampered off home for a well-deserved drink of milk. (Besides, I wanted to be sitting in my basket by the fireplace for when Santa arrived.)

And that was that. You may not believe it, but I saw it all. And it happens in Newcastle every Christmas Eve.

You'd never know it, would you? All those statues, standing so still, all year long. You would never dream of the things they do each Christmas Eve … but I know.

And now you know too.

So next time you're going past the Stephenson Monument, you might just notice that one or two of his mates still have traffic cones on their heads.

And if you look up at Earl Grey, high above the streets, you might see a little smile on his face ... he'll be thinking of the fun he'll get up to next Christmas Eve when Newcastle once again becomes – Tinseltoon.

And you never know ... if you call up to him and give him a friendly wave he might just look down and wave back at you!

The four statues on Northumberland Street, just opposite Saville Row, are Thomas Bewick, Harry Hotspur, Sir John Marley and Roger Thornton.

'Wor' Jackie Milburn, famous football star of the 1950s, has a statue on Strawberry Place beside the football ground.

The lone miner, on his way home from work, stands on top of Burt Hall, Northumberland Road, opposite the City Hall.

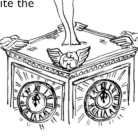

George Stephenson's monument is near the Central Station. At his feet rest four friends: the railway engineer, the track-layer, the coal miner and the blacksmith.

Queen Victoria sits in imperial non-amusement outside St Nicholas' Cathedral.

The golden fairy pirouettes on the Golden Clock outside the Northern Goldsmith's on Pilgrim Street.

St George and the dragon are locked in battle on their plinth in Old Eldon Square.

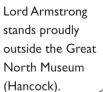

Lord Armstrong stands proudly outside the Great North Museum (Hancock).

King Neptune stands with his trident on the old Fish Market on the Quayside, just beyond the Swing Bridge.

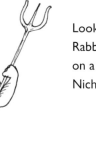

Look out for the 'Vampire Rabbit' with the big teeth on a building behind St Nicholas' Cathedral.

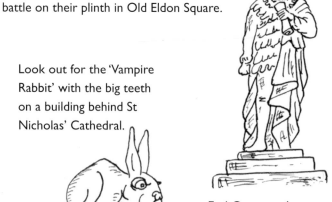

Earl Grey watches over the city from his tall column at the top of Grey Street.